Paul Ensom was educated at Bembridge School on the Isle of Wight and at Leicester University. Following his appointment as Assistant Curator at the Dorset County Museum, Dorchester, in 1978, he became deeply involved in the geology of Dorset, particularly in the Purbeck strata and their fauna of dinosaurs and other vertebrates. Between 1981 and 1988 he was sub-editor (Geology) for the *Proceedings of the Dorset Natural History and Archaeological Society*. He moved to the Yorkshire Museum, York, in 1988 as Keeper of Geology and at the beginning of 1998 he took up the post of Head of Curation (Palaeontology) at the Natural History Museum, London. He has written and contributed to numerous notes and articles on aspects of the geology of Dorset.

Following page
Purbeck strata exposed in the cliffs of Durlston Bay. A little to
the left of the photograph, Samuel Beckles is believed to
have dug his 'mammal pit' in 1857 (see illustration on page 55).
In the background are the Chalk cliffs below
Ballard Down, Swanage Bay.

DISCOVER DORSET

GEOLOGY

PAUL ENSOM

THE DOVECOTE PRESS

Teeth of small, meat-eating, dinosaurs with characteristic
serrated edges. The larger specimen is about 4 mm long.

First published in 1998 by The Dovecote Press Ltd
Stanbridge, Wimborne, Dorset BH21 4JD

ISBN 1 874336 52 0

© Paul Ensom 1998

Paul Ensom has asserted his right under the Copyright Designs
and Patent Act 1988 to be identified as author of this work

Series designed by Humphrey Stone

Typeset in Sabon by The Typesetting Bureau
Wimborne, Dorset
Printed and bound by Baskerville Press, Salisbury, Wiltshire

A CIP catalogue record for this book is available
from the British Library

5 7 9 8 6 4

CONTENTS

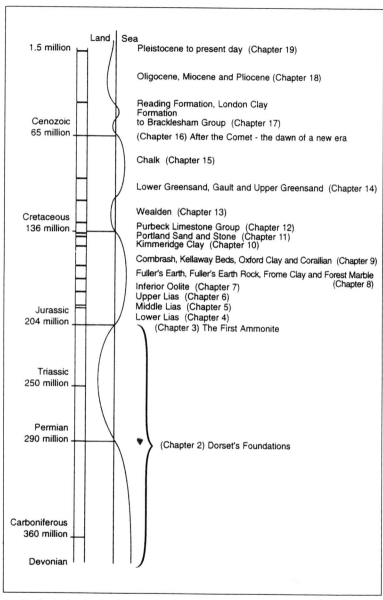

Geological column for Dorset showing main periods of geological time with simplified sea level curve alongside.

INTRODUCTION

Dorset's rocks provide a fascinating account of much that has happened during the last 200 million years. Locked within them are numerous stories which can be read like the pages of a book. The record of the rocks is not always clear or complete, sometimes millions of years are missing; much is still to be discovered.

This brief guide is written for all lovers and explorers of Dorset's glorious landscapes, for those with an enquiring mind, or those who desire an armchair acquaintance with the county of Dorset and an appreciation of how so much of man's history in the county is intimately bound up with the rocks.

In writing this guide, I have attempted to open windows with unusual views of the geological history of the area, aspects which have fascinated me and which will not necessarily have reached the wider public. Inevitably much of this guide is drawn from the magnificent coastal sections which allow us to explore in so much detail the layer-cake of geological time.

Suggestions for Further Reading and a Glossary (words in the Glossary are printed in bold when first used in the text) are included at the end of the guide.

WARNING: Reference to localities in this book does not indicate the existence of a right of access. Permission should be obtained before entering private property. Local bye-laws and the Countryside Code should be observed at all times and it is recommended that before carrying out fieldwork, the *Geological Fieldwork Code* should be read. Copies are available from the Geologists Association, Burlington House, Piccadilly, London WIV OJU. Please enclose a stamped and addressed envelope with your request.

Fieldwork is a hazardous occupation. Sensible clothing, stout footwear and an hard hat are essential. Before going onto the coast, tide timetables should be consulted and advice taken on access etc. Parts of the Dorset coast are inaccessible at high water and many of the cliffs are both precipitous and unstable.

Collecting specimens bestows a certain responsibility on the collector. You may collect a specimen of great importance. Recording where it came from and other details is a sensible policy, ensuring the full scientific value of a specimen can be realised.

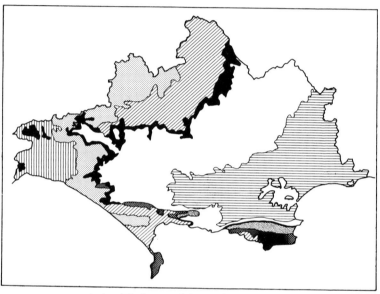

A simplified map of the geology of Dorset.

Tertiary rocks (clays, sands & gravels).

Chalk (limestone).

Lower Greensand, Gault & Upper Greensand (clays & sands).

Wealden (clays, silts, sands & grits).

Portland Sand & Stone & Purbeck Limestone Group (limestones & clays).

Kellaways Beds, Oxford Clay, Corallian & Kimmeridge Clay (limestones & clays).

Inferior Oolite, Fuller's Earth, Frome Clay, Forest Marble & Cornbrash (limestone & clays).

Lower, Middle & Upper Lias (thin limestones, clays, silts & sands).

I. DORSET'S GEOLOGY

Visitors to Dorset cannot fail to be impressed by the variety of landscapes which they confront as they explore the county. These variations have provided the inspiration for artists such as John Constable, Paul Nash, Charles Rennie Mackintosh and Frederick Whitehead, and for writers like William Barnes and Thomas Hardy whose Egdon Heath, the downs and unforgiving ground of Break Heart Hill and the Vale of the Small Dairies all owe their existence to the structures and rocks at and below the surface.

Dorset's landscape provides the briefest of glimpses of a great continuum. The oldest rocks we see at the surface are around 200 Ma (Ma stands for *million years old*), a tiny fraction of the earth's 4,500 Ma history. We have been able to suggest, and in some cases confirm, a great deal about what underlies the surface veneer of sediments less than 200 Ma.

To begin to grapple with the rocks of Dorset, the shortest of introductions to the fundamental processes which have produced them is needed. The surface of the earth is composed of numerous plates of rock. Some of these plates are denser than others. The denser plates underlie the oceans and are created from molten rock along mid-ocean ridges. They are destroyed as they sink down under the less dense rocks which make up the continents; sometimes they push continental plates ahead of them. Collisions between plates produce uplift and mountain chains are born. Sometimes a continent is torn apart and new oceans form. The continents are constantly being eroded and the sediments transported either to the oceans or to subsiding areas within continents. Continental margins and the interiors may sag and be inundated with water. Not only do continents rise and fall, but sea levels do as well, something with which we are becoming well acquainted!

Dorset sits on a continental plate which has evolved over millions of years and has been subjected to many of these processes. What is now tilted or sharply folded was once flat; what is now above sea level has frequently been below.

Dorset's very varied and at times complex geological history has provided a wide range of rock types which support many different habitats, different styles of farming and human settlement. These same rocks represent an incredible spectrum of environments in which the sediments were laid down, from ocean to shallow sea, coastal lagoon and freshwater lake, to debris fans and huge rivers. These rocks which represent such varied conditions, contain the remains of the invertebrate and vertebrate animals which have populated this county before us, some common, some very rare. Fossilised remains of fish, amphibians, reptiles, including the giant Jurassic 'sea-dragons', dinosaurs and pterosaurs all occur. Fossil mammals are preserved in rocks of four different geological periods ranging over some 167 Ma, something not found in any other county in the United Kingdom. Dorset has provided many of the finest specimens in museum collections in Britain and around the world over the last 200 years and remains a focus for numerous different fields of research.

Opposite page Diagram showing the processes and environments which produce different rocks. The numbers in brackets give the chapters in which examples can be found. 1. Pull of descending oceanic crust stretches plate leading to new crust forming at mid-ocean ridge; 2. Mountain building (1); 3. Friction and melting of rocks; 4. Igneous intrusions rise towards surface (2); 5. Deep burial and metamorphism (2); 6. Granite: e.g. Dartmoor; 7. Volcanic lavas (2); 8. Volcanic ash falls (8); 9. Deep ocean muds and silts (2); 10. Flash floods on hills (2); 11. Deserts with sand dunes and debris flows (2); 12. Occasionally isolated water mass with evaporites: e.g. salt, gypsum (2,12); 13. Active faults (6); 14. Earthquake triggered slumps (3); 15. Deeper and quieter water with fine grained sediments, occasionally organic-rich: e.g. Lower Lias, Kimmeridge Clay and Chalk (4,10,15); 16. Shallow sea with shelly limestones, muds, silts, sands and pebble beds (5,7,8,9,14,17); 17. Landslides (14,19) and burning cliff (4), (10); 18. Warm shallow seas with oolite shoals (7,9,11); 19. Coastal flats occasionally inundated by the sea with brackish lagoons, freshwater lakes, swamps and sparse tree cover (12); 20. Rivers carrying gravels, sand, silts, mud and occasional carcasses of dead animals (13); 21. Eroding land surfaces (13,14,17,18,19); 22. Ice caps on hills (19).

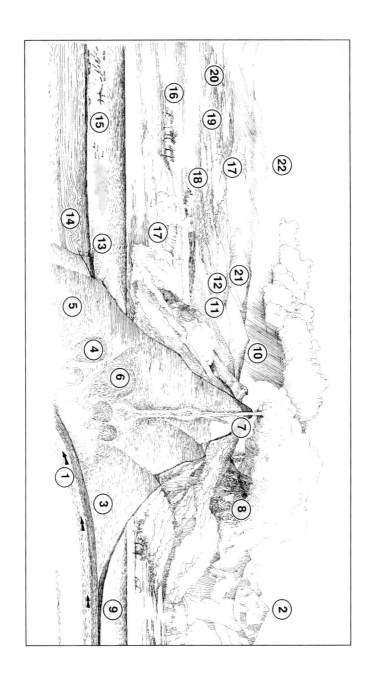

Inevitably, in an account dealing with geology, the reader will be exposed to terms which are the basis of description used by geologists, and quite foreign to them. Despite the glossary at the end of the book, a brief explanation of the most fundamental terms is provided here.

The last 550 Ma of geological time is divided into three eras, the Palaeozoic (550-250 Ma), Mesozoic (250-65 Ma) and Cenozoic (65 Ma to present). These are divided into periods, for example, the Mesozoic has three periods, the Triassic, Jurassic and Cretaceous. Each period is represented by rock units which are given names. These may be based on the properties of the rock as in the 'Cornbrash' which provided good soils for cultivating cereals, or a location like the 'Kimmeridge Clay' Formation after the tiny village on the Dorset coast, and Purbeck Limestone Group from the Isle of Purbeck. The reader should not be too concerned with terms such as Group, Formation, Member and Bed; they are labels used by geologists for layers of sediment ranging from hundreds of metres to a few centimetres in thickness!

The account begins with the oldest rocks and concludes with the most recent.

2. WINDOWS ON THE PAST: OUR FOUNDATIONS REVEALED

Time: 380-204 Ma
Latitude: 19° S - 30° N.
Climate: Hot and humid equatorial becoming arid.
Environment: Marine (Dev. & Carb.) becoming terrestrial (Perm. & Trias.) with extensive deserts, flooded by the sea at close.
Periods: Devonian, Carboniferous, Permian and Triassic.
Rocks: Limestones, Muds, breccias, conglomerates silts and sands. Salt.

During the last 500 Ma, Dorset has drifted from far south of the equator to its present position at 51° 43′N. As this long journey north has taken place, some of the **sediments** which had been deposited have been subjected to great forces. One event was especially important, the **Hercynian Orogeny**. The east-west folds and **faults** which developed then have continued to influence what happens on the surface; our past and present landscapes are echos of momentous events in our geological history.

Between 370 and 308 Ma ago two super-continents **Gondwanaland** and **Laurasia** collided to form the even bigger super-continent of **Pangaea**. Southern Britain lay on the northern edge of the ocean basin which separated these two landmasses. As this ocean closed, the sediments on its floor were folded and faulted and molten rock from deep below moved towards the surface as **igneous intrusions,**

Above The miniature map of Dorset shows the location of boreholes. Zone 1 is underlain by Carboniferous Limestones, Zone 2 Devonian sediments and Zone 3 by mainly metamorphosed Devonian and Carboniferous sediments.

[13]

the eroded tops of which form the moors of south-west England today. The often severely deformed **Devonian** and **Carboniferous** rocks resulting from these processes can be seen at the surface in Cornwall and Devon (Cornubia). During the **Permian**, volcanoes erupted in east Devon. The mountains formed at this time were later eroded, primarily during the **Permo-Triassic**. Travelling from the west, these uplifted and eroded rocks slope down to the east and are covered by progressively younger sediments; in Dorset

Permian breccia (*c.*280 Ma) composed of fragments of metamorphosed Devonian sediments from below Wytch Farm.

How parts of southern Britain may have looked during a warm and wet interlude during the Triassic period. Plants include conifers, ginkgos, ferns, tree ferns, horsetails and cycads.

these foundations are deeply buried.

But all is not lost! For over 60 years the search for oil, gas and even coal has continued, mostly across central and southern Dorset. The boreholes which have been drilled occasionally penetrate deep down to reach the **basement** rocks. The fragmentary evidence from such holes and the information which can be obtained from **seismic** and other **geophysical surveys** permits some understanding of our foundations.

Exploratory oil well being drilled by AMOCO above West Chaldon in 1997.

What we find is not unexpected, given the rocks exposed in Devon to the west. Devonian and Carboniferous rocks are present at a number of sites. Devonian rocks 2,743 m. below the surface at Wytch Farm consist of **metamorphosed** muds. They are older rocks which had been folded, faulted and eroded, forming a landscape which was eventually buried beneath Permian and Triassic rocks.

The landscape with its numerous east - west faults and associated rift valleys may have looked similar to the rift valleys of East Africa today, with a climate akin to that of the Middle East. The older rocks are overlain by **breccias** of Permian age, deposited as **debris flows** from eroding uplands during heavy rain in arid desert conditions. Similarities with sediments of the same age in Somerset to the north are likely, with a deposit of salt present in central southern Dorset. The strange **anticlinal** dome at Compton Valence just west of Dorchester attracted the attention of an oil exploration company in 1948 because they thought salt was rising towards the surface, doming the rocks above and producing a potential oil-trap at the same time.

The arid plains were occasionally swept by ephemeral rivers which along with the sands and muds carried the remains of amphibians and reptiles. The red rocks seen along the south-east Devon coast are deep beneath our feet in Dorset. Amongst them, the sandstones of the Sherwood Sandstone Group (Triassic) are the lower and major reservoir rock for Europe's largest onshore oil field at Wytch Farm. At the time of writing, AMOCO were drilling from West Chaldon out under Weymouth Bay targeting the 'Arkell Prospect', a potential reservoir in the same Triassic sandstones.

The red Permo-Triassic rocks which surface just over the border in Devon are capped by sediments laid down in a shallow sea which gradually extended across the UK around 207 Ma ago, the first time that this area of land had been submerged for around 100 Ma.

3. THE FIRST AMMONITE

Time: 204 Ma.
Latitude: 30° N.
Climate: Tropical.
Environment: Shallow marine.
Formation: Lower Lias.
Rocks: Muds and limestones.

Psiloceras planorbis, the first ammonite to appear in Dorset.

The Rhaetic rocks, while not strictly speaking exposed on the Dorset coast, are present just over the county boundary in Devon. The White Lias, or Langport Member as it is now known, is a distinctive sequence of pale creamy-white limestones. At Pinhay Bay they are exposed in the core of a small **anticline** at the foot of the cliff. A series of small folds and slumps within predominantly horizontal strata may be evidence for earthquake shocks affecting the area as these beds were deposited.

The exact position of the boundary between the **Triassic** and **Jurassic** rocks has been a matter for debate for a long time. Recently the suggestion was made that the boundary should be drawn where the first **ammonite** appears. In Dorset ammonites appear at the base of the Jurassic, first represented by a smooth-shelled form called *Psiloceras planorbis*. All over the world the appearance of psiloceratid ammonites herald the dawn of a new age.

The blue-grey and black shales and limestones which make up the

Opposite page Evidence for earthquakes? Contorted strata sandwiched between undisturbed sediments (top left and bottom right) in the Triassic Langport Member at Pinhay Bay.

Lower Lias are at times crowded with ammonites. These familiar coiled fossils, belonging to the same group of animals as the nautilus and cuttlefish in today's seas, are the geologist's key to correlating rocks across wide areas; the same ammonites in different places show that the rocks are the same age, therefore they can be *correlated*. The absence of ammonites may provide tell-tale clues as to what rocks are missing. The reason for this usefulness is that they evolved new varieties quite rapidly. Knowledge of how many ammonite zones occur within a dated sequence of rocks provides a crude measure of geological time; during the Jurassic each of the 75 ammonite zones could represent approximately 800,000 years.

4. SEA DRAGONS AND VOLCANOES

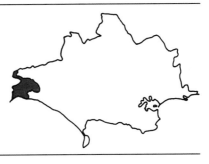

Time: 204-191 Ma.
Latitude: 30°-35° N.
Climate: Tropical.
Environment: Shallow to deeper marine.
Formation: Lower Lias (Blue Lias, Shales with Beef, Black Ven Marls, Belemnite Marls, Green Ammonite Beds).
Rocks: Clays, shales and limestones.

The Lower Lias floors the Marshwood Vale, inland from Charmouth, like a giant amphitheatre with the sides of the encircling auditorium made of the clays and sands of the Middle and Upper Lias, with hills capped by younger **Cretaceous** strata. Exposures are few, and mapping of this area has been reliant upon stream bed exposures and other rare excavations to provide the all important ammonites for identification and correlation. For those living in the vale, the clays have provided the raw materials for small scale brick, tile and pipe production. Dorset's beautiful but well-vegetated landscape gives little of the layer-cake geology away. Only from Seatown westwards does the coast provide a revealing dissection of the strata at the core of this rural vale, where the formations with names like Blue Lias, Black Ven Marls and Green Ammonite Beds are hidden beneath the green sward.

These sediments were deposited in a marine environment, in relatively shallow water, when Dorset lay at a latitude of 30° to 35° N with an average temperature of around 30°c. The seas teemed with life which the observant wanderer across the ledges west of Lyme Regis will soon see much evidence of, including gigantic ammonites scattered over the stone bands.

The 'Lyme Volcano'; the burning cliff at Lyme Regis in 1908.

The coast is characterised by cliffs which show a variety of forms, from a series of stepped terraces to near vertical faces, but always blue-grey to black with the highest boasting a startling golden-yellow capping of younger Cretaceous sediments (see Chapter 14). The different cliff profiles are the result of layers of nodules, bands of harder limestone and changes in the composition of the clays.

The lowest liassic stratum is the Blue Lias. These beds show a regular banding of harder limestones (formerly worked for cement at Lyme Regis) with inter-bedded shales, some of which are rich in organic material. These and other oil-rich shales are the source rock for the oil which is exploited in eastern Dorset around Kimmeridge and Poole Harbour. They originated on a sea-floor devoid of oxygen where plant and animal remains were not destroyed, allowing preservation of the oil which we exploit today.

Oil shales have fuelled dramatic burning cliffs at various places along the Dorset coast. Cliff falls are often a precursor of spontaneous combustion, when smoke and steam are seen rising volcano-like from fissures in the cliff. The trigger for the combustion is thought to be the rapid penetration of air to clays rich in **iron**

pyrites. This causes the pyrites to oxidise and generate heat, a process which may be enhanced by bacterial activity, triggering the spontaneous combustion of the oil-rich shales and clays. Lyme Regis was the site of one such event in 1908 which became known as the 'Lyme Volcano'. Charmouth which had previously seen activity in 1751 had steaming cliffs but no actual combustion in late 1987 and early 1988.

Amongst the inhabitants of eighteenth and nineteenth century Lyme Regis and the neighboring coastal villages, were those who eked out a living by collecting and selling fossils. The excavation of the strata from the foreshore at Lyme for the production of cement and the frequent cliff falls provided a plentiful supply of specimens, amongst which were both the unusual and the rare, including types new to science. A ready market for these natural petrifactions developed with the collectors selling to both newly formed museums and private collectors. In 1987 Taylor and Torrens described that famous daughter of Lyme, Mary Anning (1799-1847), as 'Saleswoman to a new science'. Their fascinating account tells of her discovery and sale of a new variety of fish in the context of the living standards of the time and the development of the science of geology. Shops where fossils are sold are still very much part of the local scene.

Ichthyosaurs and plesiosaurs, which in the past have been referred to as 'crocodiles' and 'sea-dragons', are some of the more spectacular marine creatures to be found fossilised in the local cliffs. These long

Ichthyosaur tail; the preserved outline is the earliest indisputable example of an ichthyosaur with a lunate caudal fin.

Scelidosaurus, a plant eating dinosaur, whose remains, and even a skin impression, have been discovered in the Liassic rocks of Dorset.

extinct reptiles could attain considerable size; the Charmouth Ichthyosaur excavated by a local collector and now in Bristol City Museum and Art Gallery is 7.5 m. long. Exceptionally, soft parts are preserved, as was demonstrated with the discovery in 1992 of the outline of the tail of a small ichthyosaur in a nodule from Charmouth.

Despite the marine origin of these rocks, the occurrence of partial skeletons and even skin impressions of plant-eating dinosaurs, the remains of an early pterosaur and larger pieces of fossilised wood, testify to land not so far away. The Cornubian landmass is thought to have been the source of exceptionally well preserved insects, including the earliest moth-like insect, which are found in nodules from these beds.

5. THE BRITTLE STAR CATASTROPHE

Time: 191-190 Ma.
Latitude: 30°-35° N.
Climate: Tropical.
Environment: Marine, at times shallow with major storms.
Formation: Middle Lias (Three Tiers, Eype Clay, Downcliff Sands, Thorncombe Sands, Marlstone Rock Bed).
Rocks: Clays, silts, sands and limestones.

The predominantly muddy **sediments** of the Lower Lias are succeeded by the much more silty and sandy Middle Lias. Golden Cap best shows the three prominent beds of sandstone which form the buttress approximately a third of the way up the cliff called the Three Tiers. The base of the lowest of these more or less coincides with the boundary of the Lower and Middle Lias. The rocks above range from clays to silty clays and sands, evidence of a marine environment which is thought to have been shallower, much more energetic and periodically subjected to storms. The sources for the sandy sediments are thought to be islands over what is now Cornwall and south Wales, and to a lesser extent a landmass which stretched from parts of East Anglia and South-East England across the southern North Sea and into Europe.

The cliffs on either side of Eype Mouth, a small village nestling close to the coast south-west of Bridport, between Thorncombe Beacon to the west and Watton Cliff to the east, provide a wonderful section through the Middle Lias. Inland exposure is poor, though spring lines around the eastern side of the encircling hills of

Marshwood Vale, which are the result of more porous sands and silts overlying impervious clays, provide clues as to the whereabouts of the various beds.

The Three Tiers are followed by the Eype Clay, which shows a return to quieter and probably somewhat deeper water. Some fossil ammonites collected from this clay have had bites taken out of their shells. This fossil vandalism has been laid at the door of crustaceans which are likely to have been common at the time; circumstantial evidence for this comes from the numerous crustacean burrows which are abundant at certain horizons in the overlying sediments.

As the deposition of the Eype Clay drew to a close, a catastrophe occurred which saw vast numbers of brittle stars, a delicate variety of starfish, overwhelmed by fine silt and sand. They were the victims of a suffocating blanket of sediment swept in by a major storm from which there was no escape. For the last 100 years or so, these fossils have been collected from the aptly named Starfish Bed which provides such a dramatic snapshot of life and death 190 Ma ago. Within the same bed is a surface where, during a slight lull in the

Traces of burrows in the sediment made by a crustacean. Fossils similar to this are common in Middle Lias silts and sands near Eype Mouth.

Fossil brittle star from the Starfish Bed.

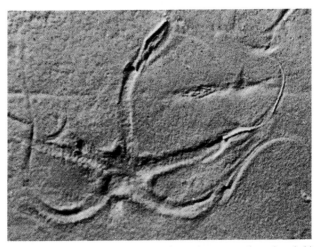

As brittle stars were swept over the sediment surface they left
a variety of impressions on the sediment surface. The ends
of their arms were sometimes snapped off and left behind.

deposition of the sediment, dead or nearly dead brittle-stars drifted
over the surface, rolling and bouncing along and leaving distinctive
traces. Evidence for similar storms is found in rocks of the same age
in Yorkshire.

A fossil sun-star collected from the Middle Lias
in the 1990s. The specimen appears to have had
19 arms and may be new to science.

A recently discovered Sun-star, a starfish with many arms, is the first recorded occurrence in the Middle Lias of Dorset. The preservation of such fragile animals is almost entirely attributable to rapid burial.

The overlying Downcliff and Thorncombe Sands tell a continuing story of a periodically stormy environment where sands and silts dominate. **Trace fossils** are often common. At some horizons evidence exists for an already **lithified** sediment on or below the sea floor which was being uncovered, broken up and rolled about to form pebbles. These were then attacked by rock-boring **bivalves**. Sometimes the pebbles and cobbles were encrusted by other animals looking for a secure home. Frequently in this sequence evidence exists for fault activity causing localised movement of the sea-floor.

The Middle Lias sediments are capped by another intriguing deposit called the Marlstone Rock Bed, which at times is an iron-rich **conglomeratic** limestone showing strong evidence of very slow deposition and even erosion. **Belemnites** and other coarse shells were being bored before burial. The surface of this bed is planed off and the Upper Lias Junction Bed is often firmly welded to it.

6. DORSET AT THE THIN END
OF THE WEDGE

Time: 190-180 Ma.
Latitude: 30°-35° N.
Climate: Tropical.
Environment: Marine.
Formation: Upper Lias (Junction Bed,
Downcliff Clay, Bridport Sands).
Rocks: Limestones, clays, silts and sands.

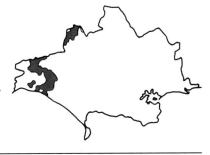

Fault controlled deposition in the Middle Lias seems likely, but the Upper Lias which succeeds has a remarkable tale to tell. Across west Dorset, the lower portion is called the Upper Lias Junction Bed. On the coast west of Eype Mouth it is a 0.6 - 1.5 m. thick, pale pink to white fine grained limestone containing four and a bit ammonites zones which represent over 3 million years. In Yorkshire the equivalent strata are predominantly black shales and mudstones with a thickness of over 100 m. While Yorkshire's marine basin subsided steadily, the sea-floor across west Dorset did not, remaining isolated from supplies of normal sand and clay sediment. The **calcium carbonate** muds which had been lithified were periodically subjected to erosion. Embedded ammonites were truncated and or reworked; **stromatolites** occasionally grew over the surfaces forming characteristic finely banded deposits mounding over surfaces or encasing fossils.

The cliff section at West Cliff between West Bay and Eype Mouth provides clear evidence that the Eypemouth Fault was active at the time. The Junction Bed thickens in a series of steps, and great blocks on the shore have in the past shown fractures with sediment from the

Fault Corner at West Cliff. Middle Jurassic sediments are faulted down against Lower Jurassic sediments. The fault was active 190 million years ago.

sea floor washed or sucked into the fissures as they opened. A great deal of geological detective work has gone into unravelling this complex deposit. The consensus is that the faults bordered a deeper basin to the south in which clays were accumulating. In north Dorset and into Somerset the components of the Middle Lias-Upper Lias Junction Bed thicken and where boreholes have penetrated these sediments to the east, they find thicker and more silty deposits.

The remaining part of the Upper Lias is no less extraordinary. The traveller from the Cotswolds to Dorset might reasonably assume that the Cotswold Sands are the same age as the apparently identical Midford, Yeovil and Bridport Sands, but not so! While the **condensed** limestone of the Upper Lias Junction Bed was forming in Dorset, in the Cotswolds of Gloucestershire a thick deposit of fine grained silt and sand was laid down. Through time the area of sand deposition moved south. The sedimentary environment responsible for this sand is still keenly debated. Suggestions include a southward migrating coastal sand bar or a series of lobes of sand fed from a south-westerly or perhaps north-easterly source.

What is beyond doubt is that the Bridport Sands provide the substance of the startling golden-yellow cliffs between West Bay and Southover near Burton Bradstock. Inland these sands form a belt which runs up to Yeovil, a strip of country with steep sided hills and sunken lanes whose banks are lined with horizontal bands and lumps of harder rock left standing proud after centuries of weathering. At Burton and East Cliffs on the coast these are a characteristic feature occurring where the sand grains have been **cemented** by the mineral calcite. The complex patterns of intricate burrows of animals, probably crustaceans, which found refuge in these sands can be seen weathering out of these cemented sands.

In the east of the county, the Bridport Sands, now more than 900 metres below the surface, form the middle reservoir in the Wytch Farm Oilfield.

7. OF SNUFF-BOXES AND SPONGES

Time: 180-170 Ma.
Latitude: 35° N
Climate: Tropical.
Environment: Shallow marine.
Formation: Inferior Oolite.
Rocks: Limestones.

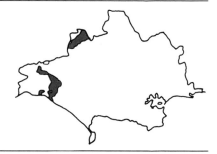

While the Bridport Sands currently play a part in the supply of fuels to the twentieth century inhabitants of Dorset, the succeeding Inferior Oolite has provided the more fundamental resource of building stones over many centuries. The numerous quarries along the outcrop are testament to a previous commercial value. The name *Inferior* Oolite has nothing to do with stone quality and everything to do with the formation's stratigraphic position *beneath* the Great Oolite. The *Oolite* refers to the abundance of **ooliths** in many of the limestones which contain a wealth of fossils representing a diverse marine fauna including **bryozoans, brachiopods,** ammonites, belemnites, **gastropods,** bivalves and **echinoids.**

The Inferior Oolite is a relatively thin formation, less than 2 m. in parts of the south to *c.*20 m. in the north near Sherborne. As with the preceding Middle and Upper Lias there is little doubt that deep seated faults were controlling deposition, occasionally fracturing the sea-floor and trapping sediment and fossils in a similar way to that seen in the Junction Bed at West Cliff (Chapter 6). Most of Dorset received little sediment and condensed limestones accumulated. The beds are often iron-rich and this gives rise to the orangey colour in much of the sequence.

Burton Cliff with Bridport Sands overlain by Inferior Oolite
and Lower Fuller's Earth Clay.

One bed consisting of vast numbers of snuff-boxes, is especially unusual. These rusty coloured, discus-sized **concretions** are tumbled higgledy-piggledy together. Fallen blocks occasionally found below the precipitous Burton Cliff demonstrate this chaotic relationship. Inland the same bed has been exposed. The study of fresh specimens allows their origin to be considered. When broken in two, the thin layers of iron-rich sediment which have been wrapped around some large piece of broken shell or other fossil are clearly seen. These laminae do not surround the whole specimen, but occur on one surface or the other. Close examination reveals the presence of **serpulid worms** and other **encrusters** on these surfaces. Stromatolites similar to those present in the Upper Lias Junction Bed were producing and trapping sediment in thin layers. The orientation of the nodules during growth is questioned by different researchers. There is agreement that these curious concretions formed on a

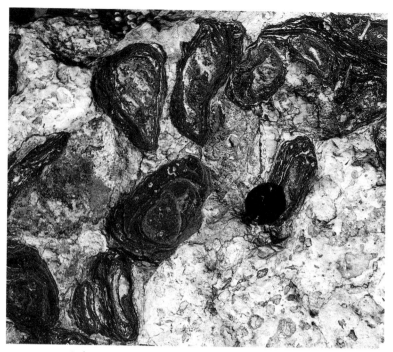

Inferior Oolite limestone containing 'snuff-boxes'.

sediment starved sea-floor and that they appear to have been turned over from time to time, possibly by severe storms, strong currents or even large marine scavengers rooting around for prey.

The word reef will for many conjure pictures of corals on the Great Barrier Reef and island atolls in the oceans of today. Through geological time many other organisms have formed reefs. Sponges are one such group and within the upper part of the Inferior Oolite there are two beds rich in these fossils which crop out at Shipton Gorge and Burton Bradstock. Numerous different types are recorded. Collectively they provided habitats for other animals which were sheltered by, or lived attached to them.

Like the Lower Lias, and despite its marine origin, the Inferior Oolite has yielded the remains of dinosaurs. The remains of two species of the flesh-eating dinosaur *Megalosaurus* have been discovered near Sherborne.

8. THE TRACKS OF LIFE AND HURRICANES

Time: 170-160 Ma.
Latitude: 35° N
Climate: Tropical.
Environment: Marine, deeper and shallower water. Occasional severe storms.
Formations: Fullers Earth, Fullers Earth Rock, Frome Clay and Forest Marble.
Rocks: Clays, sandy limestones and limestones.

The shallow clear waters of the Inferior Oolite sea were replaced by deeper waters in which muds of the Fuller's Earth Clays were deposited across much of southern Dorset. This apparent deepening was not the result of a rise in sea level, but linked with subsidence of the continental shelf upon which the marine sediments were laid down.

The name Fuller's Earth comes from a bed, near Bath, composed of the clay mineral montmorillonite in strata of the same age. This important economic deposit has been used for degreasing or fulling wool, and as the basis of **drilling muds**; it represents ash-falls from volcanic eruptions probably to the west, though the exact location of the volcano is still debated. These ash-rich clays have not been found in the Dorset succession. Fuller's Earth Clays were used for brick-making at Powerstock near Bridport.

In southern Dorset the Lower Fuller's Earth Clay is visible at the top of Burton Cliff near Burton Bradstock but is otherwise poorly exposed. The lower clays sometimes yield large numbers of the small thin shelled bivalve *Bositra buchi* which researchers have suggested were able to swim and drift in the water, avoiding the often soupy mud on the sea floor.

In the north-west of the county, a rubbly limestone called the Fuller's Earth Rock occurs in the middle of the clays south and east of Sherborne. This limestone contains a varied fauna of ammonites and bivalves.

The uppermost part of the succession, previously called the Upper Fuller's Earth Clay, has been renamed the Frome Clay. Within this clay are horizons rich in brachiopods and in the Weymouth Anticline 5 m. thick oyster banks are preserved. Oyster banks of the same age provide an upper reservoir in the Wytch Farm Oilfield. The Frome Clay forms the bulk of the dark cliffs at West Cliff immediately west of West Bay and is faulted-down against the older Bridport Sands on the eastern side of the harbour.

The Boueti Bed, named after a brachiopod which occurs in profusion, lies at the junction of the Frome Clay and the overlying Forest

Shelly limestones in the Forest Marble at West Cliff.

Ripple marks preserved on a slab of sandy-limestone from the Forest Marble. The meandering trace of an enigmatic invertebrate can be seen on the surface.

Marble, named after Wychwood Forest in Oxfordshire. The term Marble comes from beds of limestone which took a high polish, one of the attributes of a true marble. The use of the term 'Marble' is misleading as the limestones are not metamorphic marbles formed by the alteration of limestones by heat and immense pressure when deeply buried. In Dorset the Forest Marble has long been a source of durable stone used for buildings and field walls, flag stones and door steps. Thin sandy limestone tiles have been used for roofing. Examples of Forest Marble used in these ways are concentrated along the outcrop around the core of the Weymouth Anticline, along the north-west south-east coastal escarpment which runs from Abbotsbury to Burton Bradstock and inland to Bothenhampton. The east-west trending outcrops of south Dorset then disappear beneath younger Cretaceous strata to reappear at Rampisham then pass east and north to Henstridge just in Somerset. The same outcrop once supported an important lime-producing industry.

A small **outlier** of Forest Marble is preserved at West Cliff providing a good location to view some of the different sediments which make up this formation.

The Forest Marble represents a shallowing of the sea. The shelly limestone was once thought to form a single continuous bed. Mapping has shown that this bed is composed of discrete lenses and sheets near the middle of the Forest Marble, a formation in which clays predominate. They are the result of severe tropical storms, perhaps hurricanes, which swept huge volumes of shells and other invertebrates together and deposited them very rapidly. Pieces of tree are sometimes present along with the remains of frogs, salamanders, turtles, lizards, crocodiles, dinosaurs, pterosaurs, mammal-like reptiles and mammals; perhaps these were the unfortunate victims of these storms.

Sandy limestone tiles are common in the clays above the limestones and are notable for beautifully preserved ripple marks and other **sedimentary structures**. In addition the traces of animals living in and on these relatively shallow water sediments are common. Some trace fossils still puzzle experts trying to explain how they were made, an example of the present not always providing a key to the past.

9. DORSET ALL AT SEA: TURTLE STONES AND ROLLER SAND

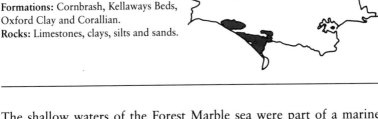

Time: 160-145 Ma.
Latitude: 36° N
Climate: Tropical.
Environment: Marine conditions; deep water to tidal shallows and lagoons.
Formations: Cornbrash, Kellaways Beds, Oxford Clay and Corallian.
Rocks: Limestones, clays, silts and sands.

The shallow waters of the Forest Marble sea were part of a marine continuum which was to last for some 70 Ma from the Rhaetic through to the deposition of the Portland Limestone. Overlying the Forest Marble is the Cornbrash, a sequence dominated by cream coloured rubbly limestones which are often very fossiliferous. The name of this formation was coined as 'corn brash' in 1813 in recognition of its suitability for cereal production.

Throughout the formation evidence points to slow deposition in a shallow offshore sea with frequent reworking of the sediments. In north Dorset an already lithified Cornbrash sea floor was eroded and the pebbles which resulted were bored and encrusted by a fauna of serpulid worms, bryozoans and bivalves.

The limestones were not of sufficient quality for **ashlar stone** but are found used as rubble stone, for road building and in the production of lime.

The relatively shallow-water conditions of the Cornbrash were replaced by deeper water conditions in which the Kellaways Beds were deposited. Rarely visible now except in the banks of streams, they were once well exposed in brick-pits near Chickerell and Rampisham, revealing silty and sandy clays with ammonites and other fossils. This initial **transgression** is a forerunner of the more significant rise in sea level associated with the Oxford Clay. The heavy clay soils which characterise this formation are a dramatic contrast to those of the Cornbrash.

The Oxford Clay forms a low cliff at Tidmoor Point on the Fleet near Chickerell. At Crook Hill, Chickerell, it was worked for bricks until 1969. Higher levels form the much landslipped cliff at Jordan Hill to the east of Weymouth. Inland it floors many of the valleys from the Weymouth lowlands to the western part of the Blackmore Vale.

The detailed mapping of these clays is hampered by poor exposure. The low-lying valleys mean that little of the clay is exposed, nor has the recent decline of the local brick industry helped. The digging of trenches for pipelines has provided the much needed 'key-hole surgery' for an internal examination especially in the north of the county. These excavations often turn up spectacular examples of 'turtle stones'. These are **septarian nodules** which may span the width of a trench and resemble the shell of a turtle! Such substantial objects in a trench can cause serious problems for excavators. In 1818 polished septarian nodules were referred to as Melbury Marble (after Melbury Osmond/Samford) and records exist of cut and polished specimens from the shores of the Fleet being used as table tops.

The Oxford Clay is often fossiliferous with large numbers of bivalves and ammonites. In some of the beds they are squashed flat, but in others they occur as beautiful three-dimensional specimens. Sometimes the mother-of-pearl shell is preserved. The remains of starfish, **crinoids**, fish and large marine reptiles are occasionally found.

The return to shallower water conditions is heralded by the increasingly sandy sediments of the Nothe Grit exposed south of Weymouth Harbour. The succeeding sediments are a remarkable contrast to the clays which have gone before. From the quiet conditions of a muddy sea floor, Dorset is the stage for the turbulent and ever changing environments of the Corallian. Over the next 4.5

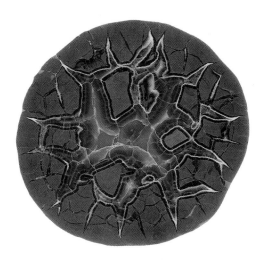

Cut and polished surface of a septarian nodule
from the Oxford Clay near Chickerell.
The nodule has a maximum diameter of 41 cm.

Ma, beds of sand, clay and limestone were deposited across the whole county in lagoonal, tidal and deeper water conditions. This cyclicity has been put down to world-wide fluctuations in sea level and local **tectonic** activity. The former is now recognised as the driving force, though **unconformities** within the Corallian of north Dorset confirm tectonics as a local ingredient.

In Dorset, Corallian strata are present on the flanks of the Weymouth Anticline, from Abbotsbury to Osmington on the northern limb and the Wyke Regis coast in the south. After disappearing from view across central-southern Dorset, they reappear in the north of the county, forming a low escarpment between Mappowder in the south via Sturminster Newton to Cucklington in the north. This low ridge is occupied by a string of villages above the flood prone lowlands of the Vale of Blackmore. Correlation of these two outcrops, despite such close proximity, has only recently been satisfactorily achieved. As the name suggests, corals are well known from this formation but more especially in counties to the north of Dorset.

Beds are frequently crowded with fossils and the thick shells of some are a testimony to the vigorous conditions in which they lived. They include bivalves, ammonites and gastropods. The clays and sands point to land not too far away; rare dinosaur bones lend support to this view. When starved of sand and clay, oolite shoals could form in the warm clear waters of this shallow sea. In the Gulf States oolites are known as roller-sand on account of a similarity to millions of minute ball bearings. During storms the oolites were swept up, moved and dumped again. The occurrence of large numbers of small sea-urchins in one such deposit may be the result of the original protective sediment blanket being removed and dropped back on top of them.

Towards the top of the formation is a fascinating bed called the Ringstead Waxy Clay representing much quieter conditions. Large delta shaped oysters which often encrust one another are common. They are sometimes bored and occasionally have other animals attached to them as they provided the only hard surface to live in and on. Exceptionally the ligaments which joined the two valves together are preserved.

At the top of the Corallian is the Ringstead Coral Bed which on the Dorset coast contains several different types of coral. These may contain holes made by rock-boring bivalves whose shells, and those of opportunistic squatters, are sometimes to be seen in these 'safe refuges'. The remains of other reef dwellers such as the large, robust spined sea urchins are also present.

The Corallian rocks have been a major source of building stone along the line of the outcrop, from Abbotsbury to Cucklington, but especially in the north of the county where the locally-named Todber and Marnhull Freestones have been widely used. Economic interest is not confined to building stones for at Bran Point near Osmington is a breached oil reservoir. Here the Bencliff Grit, which once received migrating oil from **maturing** organic-rich mudrocks, has been exposed and eroded, allowing the bulk of the oil to escape. An oily residue remains in the sands and is especially noticeable on hot summer days. An active but small oil seep is present at this location. These are clues to the complex story of oil generation and migration in the south of England, a story still being unravelled using the most advanced technology.

10. BLOOMING ALGAE AND THE ANOXIC OCEAN?

Time: 145-140 Ma.
Latitude: 38° N
Climate: Tropical.
Environment: Deep marine.
Formation: Kimmeridge Clay.
Rocks: Minor ironstone and silts, then clays, shales, coccolith and dolomitic limestones.

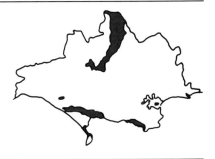

The variety of rock types seen within the Corallian are replaced by an apparently monotonous sequence of black to grey shales and clays with a maximum thickness of over 500 m. Such an appearance belies an intriguing depositional and colourful commercial history as will be revealed!

The Kimmeridge Clay is named after Kimmeridge on the Purbeck coast where magnificent cliff sections expose these beds at the core of the Purbeck **monocline**. The Kimmeridge Clay also crops out around the periphery of the Weymouth Anticline, underlying the Chesil Beach between Portland and Smallmouth. In north Dorset the Kimmeridge Clay forms a north-south strip, to the east of and echoing the outcrop of the Oxford Clay and Corallian.

At Weymouth, exposures reveal silty clays in the lowest beds and at Abbotsbury iron-rich sediments occur. The Abbotsbury Ironstone was the cause of a speculative Victorian enterprise by which ironstone was to be exported by tram line to the furnaces in South Wales. In the event the oolitic ironstone contained too much sand to be of commercial value. These ironstones are thought to represent a

Kimmeridge Clay is exposed in the cliffs of Hobarrow Bay (foreground) and Kimmeridge Bay beyond. In the distance is St Aldhelm's Head, with its impressive capping of Portland Stone.

shallow water deposit formed by the mixing of iron-rich waters with sea-water where little sediment was being deposited.

The rest of the formation consists, predominantly, of clays and shales. They are often richly fossiliferous, though many of the fossils are flattened as the muds have been compacted to as much as an eighth of their original thickness. Given the thickness of the Kimmeridge Clay this is a staggering thought! **Turtle stones** like those in the Oxford Clay are found at certain horizons. Three-dimensional fossils including ammonites in many of them are evidence for early formation before the sediment was compacted.

An extensive swathe of eastern England from Dorset to Yorkshire is underlain by Kimmeridge Clay and individual beds can be traced for hundreds of kilometres. To what do we owe such extraordinary continuity? This formation represents a period of transgression when a tranquil sea up to 100 m. deep allowed soupy muds to accumulate undisturbed over extensive areas.

The Kimmeridge Clay sea floor was periodically starved of life-giving oxygen (anoxia) which led to the death of much of the fauna and provided ideal conditions for the exceptional preservation of organisms. The absence of scavengers and other sea-floor dwellers ensured that dead organisms falling to the sea-bed remained undisturbed. These frequent cyclic events have been laid at the door of extensive algal blooms. Smaller scale blooms have affected some coasts, rivers and lakes of England, during recent warm sunny summers, 'poisoning' these aquatic environments and killing much of the fauna. The consequent accumulation of the remains of countless billions of tiny **algae** called **coccoliths** give rise to the well known White Band and other pale laminae within the Kimmeridge Clay. A more recent explanation is that ocean currents led to stratification of the water mass over wide areas leading to these anoxic bottom' conditions.

Bed-by-bed collecting by gifted local geologists such as Steve Etches and others in the last 20 years has revealed many hitherto unnoticed fossils. Tiny brittle-stars crowded together on one bedding plane, the egg cases of fish, in addition to the bones of gigantic marine reptiles, sometimes with the tooth marks left by attackers or scavengers. Scallop fishermen have dredged extraordinary numbers of reptile bones from the sea floor off Portland where they have been concentrated as a winnowed lag deposit. This provides an exciting glimpse of a process which has happened many times during geological time across Britain. The remains of dinosaurs and flying reptiles have also been collected.

The Kimmeridge Clay is economically very important. Oil shales are common and have been burnt on open fires earning the name 'Kimmeridge Coal', but sulphurous smells and high ash content have ensured only local interest! Burning cliffs are recorded, for example Holworth in 1826 and Clavell's Hard 1973/4 (see also Chapter 4). The Blackstone Band is an especially good example of an oil shale deposited on the anoxic sea floor. The waxy quality of this brownish-black shale was exploited by the prehistoric inhabitants of Dorset and more recently the Romans. 'Kimmeridge Coal Money' is often found in excavations of industrial sites both locally and further afield. These are the offcuts from shale which was turned on lathes to produce bowls and bracelets in addition to table legs and trays.

Since then, Kimmeridge has been the site of several industrial processes using the shales. During the seventeenth century glass and alum production were the subject of extraordinary legal wrangles fought out in London with imprisonment and financial ruin for those guilty of disregarding others patents or licences. Distillation of the shale in retorts produced between 11 and 66 gallons of oil from each ton of oil shale and was used for lighting. In the last century mines operated at Kimmeridge and for a while near Portesham. However man's attempts at commercial distillation were no match for the deep burial and high temperatures achieved beneath the North Sea where the Kimmeridge Clay is the source of much of the oil, providing great wealth to successive governments since the 1960s. The same rocks in Dorset have never been buried deep enough for oil maturation and its migration into oil reservoirs.

II. TITANIC AMMONITES AND 'OSSES 'EADS

Time: 140-137 Ma.
Latitude: 38° N
Climate: Tropical.
Environment: Shallow marine environments.
Formations: Portland Sand and Portland Stone.
Rocks: Dolomitic silts and sands, and limestones.

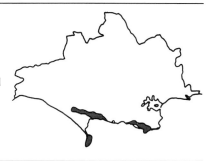

While the formations considered so far were deposited across the whole of Dorset, now comes a time when the original extent of the uppermost Jurassic and lower Cretaceous strata is open to question. Were sediments deposited over a wider area and subsequently eroded or were they confined, more or less, to their present outcrop in the south of the county, from the Isle of Purbeck in the east to Portesham in the west? Tantalisingly we see similar strata in the Vale of Wardour to the north of Dorset but boreholes have not proved these strata in Dorset north of the Chalk ridgeway from Ballard Down north of Swanage to the Bride Valley in the west. We do know that the Portland Sand Formation was deposited in a restricted marine basin and that the overlying Portland Stone Formation was a near shore deposit. The reactivation of faults in the basement (Chapter 2) is a most tempting explanation for some of these observed features.

The lower Portland Sand Formation is well exposed on the West

Opposite page West Weares, Isle of Portland. Portland Stone and overlying Lower Purbeck strata crown the cliff.

Gad Cliff: Portland Stone caps Portland Sand and Kimmeridge Clay.

Weares of Portland and Gad Cliff and Hounstout on the Isle of Purbeck. Usually with a blueish-grey colour, these are **dolomitic** sandy limestones. They contain the fossilised remains of marine animals including ammonites, indicative of normal salinities for the bulk of the water-mass when they were deposited.

The overlying Portland Stone Formation could be studied almost as easily on the streets of London and other major towns and cities as in Dorset. The reason for this is the love affair between this durable stone and many architects since Sir Christopher Wren made extensive use of it after the Great Fire of London in 1666. This century Sir Edwin Lutyens specified Portland Stone from Portland for numerous War Memorials, including the Cenotaph, built to commemorate the fallen of World War I. The extensive underground mines and cliff-side quarries on Purbeck and the enormous holes in Portland testify to its enduring popularity.

Portland Stone is a distinctive white **oolite** which contains randomly scattered thick shelled fossils and occasional wedges of stacked and arched bands. These are the fossilised remains of marine algae. They are more common in the Roach where reef-like structures were formed by the algae. The Roach is a very fossiliferous oolitic limestone confined to the north end of Portland and characterised by the moulds and casts of the numerous bivalves and gastropods whose shells have been dissolved. Amongst these are a distinctive bivalve called *Myophorella*, which the local quarrymen refer to as 'osses eads' because the casts resemble horses' heads. The famous 'Portland Screw' is a similarly preserved high-spired gastropod. The holes made by boring bivalves and sponges in these and similar shells as they lay on the sea floor can now be viewed as casts in the voids where the host shells have been dissolved.

A Portland Stone quarry near Weston on the Isle of Portland.

Titanites: giant ammonites are found in the Portland Stone.
A 1p coin provides a scale.

To the north of the high energy reef and oolite shoals, quieter waters saw the deposition of a fine grained white limestone which can be mistaken for the much younger Chalk (Chapter 15). The deception is almost complete as these rocks contain bands and nodules of the **flint**-like rock called **chert**. However, the presence of very large ammonites, including the aptly named *Titanites*, enables certain identification. These giants of the sea are frequently seen built into walls on Portland and Purbeck.

Portland chert was traded by prehistoric populations. Portland Stone is still quarried on the Isles of Portland and Purbeck to be used for decorative work, buildings and crushed aggregate for roadstone.

12. PURBECK PARK: FISHES, FROGS, DINOSAURS AND MAMMALS

Time: 137-130 Ma.
Latitude: 38° N
Climate: Sub-tropical. Pronounced wet
and dry seasons at times.
Environment: Very shallow lagoons and
lakes; occasional emergence. Hypersaline
during periods of strong evaporation.
Rare marine influences otherwise
brackish to freshwater.
Formation: Purbeck Limestone Group.
Rocks: Clays, shales, sandy limestones and limestones.

With the passing of the Portland strata, enter the Purbeck Limestone Group, a succession of limestones, shales and clays, named after the Isle of Purbeck.

For many years the boundary of the Jurassic and Cretaceous has been drawn near the middle of the Purbeck strata but recent work indicates that it would be better placed just above the Portland Limestone Formation. This uncertainty arises because no ammonites, so vital for correlation (Chapter 3), are found in the Purbeck strata which were deposited in freshwater, brackish and very rarely marine environments. Pieces of reworked fossil ammonite from the Kimmeridge Clay and pebbles of chert from the Portland Beds do occur providing conclusive evidence that uplift had occurred and erosion of earlier formations was taking place, probably north of what is now the Ridgeway.

While marine environments were rare, in the lower Purbeck salinities were abnormally high, permitting the formation of salt, gypsum and other evaporite minerals. The dissolution of a thicker layer of evaporites long after they were deposited is believed to be responsible for the jumbled layers of rock seen in the cliff above the Fossil Forest near Lulworth Cove and elsewhere. As folding of the strata occurred, the overlying strata collapsed into the hole left behind.

Our knowledge of the climate 137 Ma ago comes in part from studies of the growth rings of the celebrated fossil trees which are found in the lowest Purbeck strata. They show that periods of winter rain were succeeded by summer drought. Dorset's climate can be compared to that of parts of North Africa, the fresh-water marshes of southern Iraq and even parts of Florida today. The trees grew on low coastal flats and were periodically drowned by the sea. Sediment-producing stromatolites covered the stumps and fallen trunks forming the mounds, seen at the Fossil Forest and elsewhere. These beds are known as the 'Caps'.

Purbeck environments supported huge numbers of molluscs whose shells go to make the famous shell limestones, like the Purbeck Marble, which is composed of countless millions of snail shells. With colours ranging from green to blue-green and even pinky-red and an ability to take a high polish, this stone has been assured wide use in the Early English churches and cathedrals of England. Like the older Forest Marble this is a sedimentary marble. The Romans recognised their quality, and the quarrymen of Purbeck have continued to exploit them over hundreds of years, previously exporting them by sea from Swanage and the shores of Poole Harbour to be used for roofing, flooring, kerb-stones, tomb stones and decorative work inside buildings.

The Purbeck Limestone Group has become one of the world's most important formations for the study of vertebrates from the middle Mesozoic (Chapter 1). The history of discovery goes back to the 1850s when a local surgeon collected a tiny dinosaur jaw and some mammal remains. The retired lawyer Samuel Beckles was encouraged by Sir Richard Owen, a leading scientist of the day, to come and search for further specimens. He did this with considerable success;

Opposite page An 137 million-year-old fossil tree discovered in quarry workings on Portland. These trees were able to cope with periodic drought.

The excavation of Beckle's Mammal Pit on the cliff in Durlston Bay, Swanage. The illustration which accompanied an article by Charles Kingsley in *The Illustrated London News* in 1857 is thought to show Samuel Beckles, wearing the top hat, directing operations.

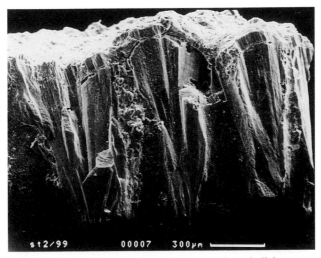

Above Cross section through a fragment of eggshell from a dinosaur or turtle. Scale bar is 0.3 mm.
Opposite page Dinosaur tracks uncovered in a quarry near Acton. They are believed to have been made by a sauropod, e.g. *Diplodocus*. Domestic broom for scale.

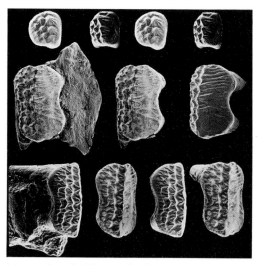

Mammal teeth: Tiny teeth of the multituberculate (many tubercles) *Albionbataar denisae*. The largest is only 1.4 mm long, the smallest 0.7 mm!

many varieties of mammal were collected from a quarry on the cliff in Durlston Bay and subsequently described by Owen. Discoveries of fish and reptiles (turtles, crocodiles, very rare dinosaurs, flying reptiles with wing spans up to 6 m.) and numerous dinosaur footprints have been made, the quarries and cliffs providing unrivaled opportunities for collecting and observing.

In 1986 a dinosaur footprint site was found with multiple tracks made by a large quadrupedal dinosaur, probably a sauropod like *Diplodocus*, and the more usual tracks of bipedal dinosaurs. The site has yielded many new and exciting finds, including frogs and salamanders which are the first amphibians to have been found in the Purbeck strata. In addition there are the teeth of meat and plant eating dinosaurs, crocodiles, pterosaurs, lizards and a primitive lizard-like reptile related to the tuatara. Over 700 tiny mammal teeth have been collected from which six new species have so far been described and links with faunas from Morocco and N. America recognised. The eggshell of dinosaurs and other reptiles is the latest extraordinary discovery; the former is a first for Britain.

13. RIVERS FROM THE NORTH AND WEST

Time: 130-113 Ma.
Latitude: 38° N
Climate: Sub-tropical.
Environment: Terrestrial dominated by rivers. Rare hints of the sea.
Formation: Wealden .
Rocks: Clays, shales, silts, sands and grits.

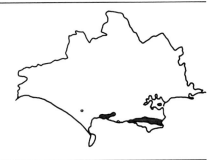

Above the Purbeck strata are the Wealden beds. Like the Portland and Purbeck strata in Dorset they are confined to the south. These soft clays, silts, sands and occasional grits floor the valleys between Swanage Bay and Durdle Door via Worbarrow and Mupe Bays and Lulworth Cove. Coastal exposures are of variable quality as vegetation covered slips obscure details of these often brightly-coloured sediments. The sands and grits provide the most impressive cliffs and also give rise to east-west ridges along the valleys. Further outcrops occur at Chaldon and Upton and as far west as the Ridgeway to the south-west of Dorchester. They thicken dramatically from west (107 m. at Upwey) to east (716 m. at Swanage). Wealden sediment is absent in the boreholes drilled around Wytch Farm on the shores of Poole Harbour. Was it ever deposited or was this a subdued upland area draining into a fault controlled basin to the south?

Wealden palaeogeography has been much debated. We are able to say that much of the sediment deposited across southern Dorset was carried by rivers probably draining upland areas to the north and west. Rock fragments thought to come from the un-roofed

Worbarrow Bay: Wealden clays, sands and grits form the broad valley between Swanage and Tyneham. The scattered blocks in the foreground are from the Upper Greensand and Lower Chalk from the cliff below Flowers Barrow.

How parts of Dorset may have looked during Wealden times. The dinosaur *Iguanodon* is seen with crocodiles and turtles.

granites of Cornubia have been identified.

At Mupe Bay is a fascinating deposit of sandstone with large cobbles and small boulders of oil-cemented sand. There is a strong probability that oil was already seeping to the surface along a fracture when the river sand was being deposited. This shows that oil generation had started and faults were active locally.

The Wealden sediments contain substantial quantities of plant debris. Fragments of charcoal are present in the sediments and researchers have shown that periodic fires swept through the vegetation. A piece of resin-like material, exuded from a Wealden tree, has been found in the coarse grits. The casts of dinosaur footprints are occasionally found on the bottom surfaces of sandstones, but rarely their bones. One may conjure a picture of the carcasses of these extinct reptiles being swept down during floods, perhaps being scavenged by other dinosaurs, decaying and finally their skeletons being scattered across river flood plains. Doubtless new discoveries await.

Wealden clays have provided the raw materials for specialist bricks and tiles and the hard iron oxide cemented grits, when available, have been used locally as a building stone.

14. DORSET IS DROWNED

Time: 113-97 Ma.
Latitude: 39° N
Climate: Sub-tropical.
Environment: Marginal marine to fully marine.
Formations: Lower Greensand, Gault and Upper Greensand.
Rocks: Limestones, clays, limestones, silts and sands. Cherts.

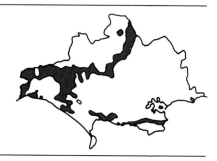

The non-marine environments which had existed for around 20 Ma with only rare marine incursions were now replaced by fully marine ones. These first manifest themselves in the poorly exposed Lower Greensand. This rests on the Wealden south of the Chalk Ridgeway, thinning to the west from Punfield Cove near Swanage, where it contains ammonites, to disappear around Lulworth. North of the Chalk is an unconformity where the Lower Greensand rests on eroded Oxford Clay beneath Arne, and Kimmeridge Clay around Child Okeford. This witnesses the progressive drowning, from south-east to north-west, of a landscape which with faulting and folding had been shaped over millions of years, as if the North Sea was spreading west over Britain today.

The Lower Greensand mix of sands and clays often contain rootlets. In the east at Swanage the Punfield Marine Band, deposited between open sea to the east and estuarine and lagoonal conditions to the west, contains well over 80 species of fossil.

The overlying Gault Clay outcrop demonstrates the complete flooding of Dorset by the sea. This thin deposit (*c.*27 - 7 m. from east to west) of sandy-clay with marine fossils is found in the west of the county resting on eroded Lias. At Compton Valence the Gault rests

A view across the Marshwood Vale to the Dorset heights.

on the Fuller's Earth and between Ringstead and White Nothe covers folded and truncated Kimmeridge Clay, Portland and lowest Purbeck strata. As we are confident that all formations from the Lias to the Kimmeridge Clay had been deposited over Dorset, this significant unconformity highlights the scale of the uplift and erosion which had taken place before the submerging of the landscape was complete.

The Gault is usually marked by spring-lines around the edges of the dissected Chalk downland escarpments from west Dorset to the

Shillingstone Gap and north to Shaftesbury, and this in turn is a zone of major landslides. In 1588 'A field of three acres, with the trees and fences, in Blackmore, moved from its place, and paffed over another field, travelling in the high-way that goeth to Herne [Cerne], and there ftayed'. Recently, prehistoric landslides have been documented from around Shaftesbury, and in the south-west the infamous coastal landslips between Culverhole Point in Devon and Charmouth are lubricated by water escaping at the contact of the Jurassic and Cretaceous sediments.

The overlying sediments of the Upper Greensand range from the greenish Foxmould and bright yellow sands with chert beds capping Pilsdon Pen, Golden Cap and the other heights of west Dorset, to green sands and rubbly sandstones in central Dorset. Around Milton Abbas and Shatftesbury, thicker beds of green sandstone have been used as an ashlar stone. These beds are often very fossiliferous and the numerous ammonites provide evidence of condensed deposition in different places at different times. Detailed studies of this complex deposit point to still active basement structures controlling sedimentation. The green colour is caused by small grains of the mineral **glauconite**.

15. THE GREAT CHALK SEA

Time: 97-65 Ma.
Latitude: 40° N
Climate: Tropical.
Environment: Marine.
Formations: Lower, Middle and Upper
Chalk.
Rocks: Limestones = Chalk.

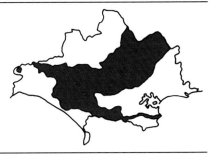

The rising sea-levels seen throughout the preceding 17 Ma are almost maintained to the end of the Cretaceous. The Chalk sea was extensive and may have been as much 200 - 300 m. above present levels around 75 Ma ago. Deposition of the Chalk spanned some 30 Ma.

The earliest Chalk deposited in west and central Dorset maintains an Upper Greensand-like quality with sandy and even gritty limestones not uncommon. An example *par excellence* is the Eggardon Grit exposed in the sides of Eggardon Hill and elsewhere in central Dorset. The sources of coarser sediment, possibly Cornubia, were soon so subdued or entirely covered by the sea, that only the abundant plankton in the sea could provide the fine calcareous ooze accumulating on the sea floor. As in the White Band of the Kimmeridge Clay, coccoliths are an important component of these startling white limestones, so familiar to those who live south-east of a line from Flamborough Head in Yorkshire to Beer Head in Devon. A significant proportion of the Chalk sediment is composed of foraminifera, the tiny shells of single-celled animals and pieces of broken up shell. The process by which the hard parts of dead animals are reduced to mud is achieved mechanically, and biologically by plants and animals which bore, dissolve and tunnel into the remains.

Shells full of tiny holes become rotten and eventually break up completely. The occurrence of the teeth of shell-crushing rays points to the involvement of fish in this recycling process.

A simple experiment will reveal some of the components of Chalk. Vigorously scrub the surface of a piece of clean soft Chalk in water. After a few minutes pour away the milky solution and add clean water to the residue. Repeat this flushing process several times until the water is clear. Look at the residue with a magnifying glass and with luck you will be able to see some of the larger microfossils and other shell debris amongst the concentrate. The Chalk is at times rich in larger fossils such as brachiopods, bivalves, ammonites, belemnites, echinoids and crinoids. Sponges are often common and are frequently found encased in flint nodules.

No other formation has such a visible impact on the Dorset landscape. Vast acreages of downland stretch from Ballard Down near Swanage as a narrow strip to Worbarrow Bay, forming cliffs beneath Flowers Barrow and at Arish Mell, then providing the spectacular vertical cliffs west from Lulworth Cove to White Nothe. The Chalk, at times vertical or even overturned, is the southern margin of the Chalk **syncline** which forms the Hampshire Basin. The edge of this great basin runs out to west Dorset then east and north towards Salisbury and Cranborne. Evidence for the settlement and rituals of prehistoric man abound across these great expanses.

To the casual observer the Chalk appears remarkably uniform. For many years the Geological Survey did little to dispel this perception, identifying only three components, the Lower, Middle and Upper Chalk. Recent detailed mapping has started to build a more refined stratigraphy, enabling the subtleties of these strata to be unravelled. Thinning of individual beds is now recognised, and the Upper Chalk so often shown on maps as being devoid of faults has been demonstrated to have its fair share after all. The uppermost Chalk is now missing from Dorset, but clues exist which point to its presence at one time (Chapter 17).

The Chalk is generally too soft to be of more than local significance as a source of building stone. Faulting and folding along the Purbeck Ridgeway has produced an especially hard variety which may have been the source of some of the white mosaic tesserae used by the

White Nothe: Chalk with its bedding clearly defined by marine erosion.

Romans. Corfe Castle is built on a Chalk knoll which owes its isolation to the superimposition of the local drainage pattern. Flint occurs as both bands of nodules and tabular layers. Palaeolithic, mesolithic and neolithic populations used flint to make implements, and it is commonly used as a building stone, especially across the outcrop.

Flint gravels derived from the Chalk (Chapters 18 & 19) are a major source of aggregate for the construction industry. While commercial values of this raw material are easily assessed, the protection provided by flint beach gravels along Dorset's coast, a first line of defence against the erosive power of the sea, is less easily costed. Extraction and grading of beach pebbles was once a small but important industry along the west Dorset coast, but growing fears concerning depletion of the beaches led to a ban being imposed as recently as the 1970's (Chapter 19).

16. AFTER THE COMET
THE DAWN OF A NEW ERA

Time: 65 Ma.
Latitude: 40°-41° N
Climate: Tropical but possibly severely perturbed in aftermath of comet impact.
Environment: Marine.
Formation: Upper Chalk.
Rocks: Absent.

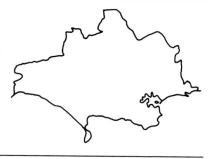

In Britain the distinctive Chalk is an eye-catching full-stop at the end of the Mesozoic era; but was there an exclamation mark? As the curtain closed on the Cretaceous period, numerous organisms became extinct. Famously the dinosaurs do not survive into the Cenozoic era, neither do the great marine reptiles nor the ammonites. The extinctions at the **K-T boundary** have been a point of discussion for a long time, but the debate has become more focussed since 1980 when the theory that the earth was hit by a comet or asteroid was first proposed. The abundance of the element iridium in a layer of sediment coincident with the boundary at sites around the world is sadly not present in the Dorset succession. Uplift and erosion has removed the uppermost layers of Chalk in Dorset and elsewhere in Britain and the nearest boundary deposit with an iridium spike is to be found in Denmark and the Mediterranean.

What might an observer in Dorset have witnessed of this event thousands of kilometres away 65 Ma ago? In the absence of any deposits, some geospeculation is required. Observations made on the impact of Comet Shoemaker-Levy 9 on the gas-giant Jupiter in 1994

An artist's representation of an asteroid impacting the surface of
the earth 65 million years ago.

have led some to suggest that an atmospheric shock-wave spread out from the impact site, preserved on the Yucatan Peninsula in Mexico, passing over much of the surface of the globe. The plume of fiery debris ejected into the atmosphere would have fallen back to earth engulfing millions of square kilometres in a global firestorm which seems likely to have passed over what is now Dorset. The great cloud of toxic chemical particles and dust ejected from the impact site into the atmosphere then enveloped the world, cutting out appreciable amounts of sunlight and triggering a nuclear winter. Fall-out from the dust cloud accumulated on the oceans floors.

Whether or not the end of the Cretaceous was punctuated by this impact, with its devastating consequences, we do know that the sediments resting on the Chalk across Dorset are very different, and the flora and fauna they contain are distinctly modern.

Chalk cliffs at St Oswald's Bay. The thin tube, low in the cliff and in the centre, is a large solution hole (see text opposite).

17. OUR BASEMENT MOVES AGAIN: FOUNDATIONS FOR THE HEATHS

Time: 65-40 Ma.
Latitude: 41° N
Climate: Sub-tropical.
Environment: Terrestrial (rivers, lakes etc.) to marine.
Formations: Reading Formation, London Clay Formation and Bracklesham Group.
Rocks: Clays, silts, sands and gravels. Rare limestones.

At the close of the Cretaceous, the blanket of Chalk was uplifted and gently folded; the Cretaceous sea-floor was exposed to erosion. This was linked to the continuing process of North Atlantic opening which had started during the Triassic, producing a gentle slope from north-west to south-east. The occurrence of Upper Greensand chert in the earliest Cenozoic sediments points to more extensive erosion not too far from Dorset, perhaps in east Devon. The Cenozoic is subdivided into the Tertiary (65-1.5 Ma) and Quaternary (1.5 Ma - present).

Sixty million years ago the area south-east of a line from East Anglia to Dorset accumulated sediments from rivers, deltas, estuaries, lagoons and the sea. The earliest Tertiary strata are missing in Dorset, though deposits resting on the Chalk in east Devon have been interpreted as a relict of this early phase of erosion, which took place while Tertiary Chalk was being deposited in the North Sea. Across Dorset the Chalk surface is frequently pock-marked with **solution holes** filled with red-brown clay containing green or black stained flints derived from the Chalk. These deposits are often exposed

Fossiliferous ironstone with flint pebbles, current aligned snails, bivalves and for the sharp eyed, a sharks tooth! From the London Clay near Wimborne. The tooth is white and at the base and centre of the photograph.

during road building and trenching schemes and are evidence of the continuing process of Chalk dissolution stretching back to the earliest Tertiary. Some solution holes are of considerable size and are termed dolines. Examples can be seen in the cliffs of St Oswald's Bay and on the heaths between Dorchester and Bere Regis which have the finest array of Chalk dolines anywhere in Britain. A good example is Culpepper's Dish on Bryants Puddle Heath which is 86 m. wide and 21+m. deep.

The earliest Tertiary formations preserved are the Reading Formation and London Clay which have a very similar extent. They are not well exposed, though the Reading Formation can be seen resting on the eroded Chalk at Studland. The Reading Formation clays are recorded as brightly coloured and mottled, a feature often associated with lagoonal environments. Around Broadmayne, close to their westerly limit, there was sufficient thickness to support an important local brick industry producing, amongst others, a distinctive pinkish brick with black splodges, now much sought after. Silts, sands and gravels also occur.

Fossils are rare, but show marine influence in the east of the county. During road building work near Wimborne pieces of fossiliferous iron-rich sandstone with drifts of flint pebbles and rare sharks teeth were recovered from the London Clay. Some surfaces had masses of high spired gastropods aligned in the same direction by the prevailing currents. The full extent of these early marine incursions over Dorset may be gauged by the occurrence of wave battered flint pebbles on Chalk downland where no recognizable Tertiary deposits are preserved.

Much of the Dorset-end of the Hampshire Basin is covered by sediments of the Bracklesham Group. These are the bedrock of the characteristic Dorset heaths. They were mostly deposited by rivers but occasional marine incursions from the east can be detected.

During these early phases of exhumation and reburial of the Chalk, earth movements played an important part. However they were only minor compared to those generated by a major reactivation of the east-west faults which had been so significant in earlier times. Around 42 Ma ago earth movements imposed new boundaries within this area, forming the London and Hampshire Basins. The rocks preserved in these elongate synclines record complex and rapid changes between marine and terrestrial environments.

Most important were fault scarps south of the line of the Chalk Ridgeway in southern Dorset. During periods of torrential rain great fans of material were flushed from an eroding upland to the south over what is now Weymouth, the Isle of Purbeck and the English Channel. At Creechbarrow near Wareham and at Bincombe between Dorchester and Weymouth large flints are present in clays and sands. At the latter site blocks of **silicified** limestone contain fossils which are only present in horizons preserved in Norfolk. At the Hardy Monument south-west of Dorchester is a thick deposit of flint and chert gravel with pebbles from the Purbeck strata which were also exposed to the south. Could the scatter of exotic pebbles from the west have been transported here by rivers flowing east at the foot of the 'Weymouth Uplands'? Were they from pebbly horizons in the eroding Cretaceous rocks or a concentration of those scattered

Dorset's answer to Hertfordshire Puddingstone: a flint breccia-conglomerate with a tough siliceous cement, a remnant of a more extensive deposit in the vicinity of the Hardy Monument.

pebbles of the Chalk uplands, all that remained of the earliest Tertiary cover?

The flint gravels are sometimes cemented by silica, the mineral of which so many of the pebbles are composed, forming a tough conglomerate. Blocks of this and other well cemented sands called **quartzites** are known as Sarsens. They occur as scatters over various downland tracts in southern Dorset and even at lower levels north of Corscombe. These massive rocks have been utilised by prehistoric man in his monuments.

The coarse sediments are replaced northwards and eastwards by sands, finer gravels and valuable deposits of ball-clay, so called because the miners made balls of the clay during extraction. Ball-clays are much in demand for the ceramics industry and are exploited from open cast pits across the Dorset heaths around Wareham; mines were once common place. The clay particles forming these deposits accumulated on tidal flats and in salt marshes having been carried by rivers draining areas where rocks were weathered in warm humid conditions to the west.

Above the ball-clays and sands is the Agglestone Grit which forms the famous Agglestone and smaller Puckstone on Studland Heath. Similar but smaller lumps of this iron-rich grit, termed 'heathstone', have been used as a building stone in and around the heaths. The cliffs around Bournemouth once yielded fabulous plant fossils indicative of humid tropical conditions. Rafts of vegetation and scattered leaves from the forests bordering the rivers drifted down-stream, becoming waterlogged and were buried in the fine muds.

Fossil palm frond from ball clay deposits around Wareham and Corfe Castle.

Sadly the remains of the animals living at the same time were rarely fossilised or are absent from this succession. The exception is a remarkable patch of the slightly younger Creechbarrow Limestone, a relic of a freshwater lake fed by run-off and springs from what may have been a faulted Chalk scarp. With evidence for rivers and non-aquatic environments, this formation provides an extraordinary window glimpsing an ecosystem normally hidden from view. Detailed research carried out between 1975 and 1986 revealed 45 species of mammal, 12 of which were new to science. Amongst their number were bats, primates, rodents, distant relatives of the horse, hippopotamus and camel.

The Creechbarrow discovery underlines the astonishing wealth of mammal sites which exist north and south of the east-west Chalk Ridgeway of the Hampshire Basin. This is no coincidence; the repeated movements along this important east-west structure have provided favourable environments in which mammals could live and be preserved as fossils. Perhaps palaeontologists should be able to predict the occurrence of mammal bearing strata just like oil geologists hazard educated guesses at where oil will be found.

Rocks of equivalent age (c.41 Ma) within the Barton Group crop out from Bournemouth eastwards to Hengistbury Head and Barton, the latter just in Hampshire. They are mostly marine sediments but show clear evidence of the close proximity of land and are the youngest Tertiary rocks exposed in Dorset. They are at times richly fossiliferous with rare terrestrial mammals drifted in from the adjacent land. Two species of whale were discovered just over the border in Hampshire.

18. DORSET'S MISSING MILLIONS

Time: 40-1.5 Ma.
Latitude: 41°-50° N
Climate: Sub-tropical but rapid cooling
after 37.5 Ma becoming temperate.
Environment: Terrestrial.
Periods: Late Eocene, Oligocene,
Miocene and Pliocene.
Rocks: Not recognised.

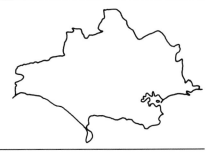

Late **Palaeogene** deposits (40-24 Ma) are present in Hampshire and on the Isle of Wight, representing the final stages of the filling of the Hampshire Basin as sea levels fell and the climate cooled. Dorset was an area of low-lying land at the western end of this area which was dominated by fresh and brackish water environments. If sediments were deposited across the County we cannot recognise them today.

These millions of missing years is further compounded by the **Neogene** period (24 - 1.5 Ma) which is virtually absent in Britain. Across the south of the country the effects of the collision between the Africa-Arabian and Eurasian Plates along the line of the Mediterranean had far reaching consequences. Great pressure was applied to the areas to the north where there had already been movement produced by weak compression during the early Tertiary, such as along the line of the Ridgeway from Swanage to Abbotsbury (Chapter 17). Now the movements become more intense and widespread. The English Channel and the fringes of southern Dorset which for so long had been an area of subsidence were ruthlessly thrust upwards. Nowhere are the results more dramatically seen than at Lulworth Cove and Stair Hole.

North of this line, some of Dorset's subsurface faults responded

A close up of the 'Lulworth Crumple' at Stair Hole, Lulworth, a dramatic testament to the great forces which have moulded the Dorset landscape.

and movement along these fractures caused further gentle folding of overlying rocks.

Gradual uplift to the west and north allowed the drainage system which had evolved during the Tertiary to be superimposed on the landscape with a predominant flow from between west and north-west to east and south-east. The erosion of Jurassic, Cretaceous and Tertiary sediments continued, and our modern landscape evolved.

19. THE BIG CHILL: ENTER MAN

Time: 1.5 Ma to present.
Latitude: 50° 43′ N
Climate: Maritime temperate but
continental dry during ice ages.
Environment: Terrestrial and marginal
marine.
Periods: Pleistocene and Holocene.
Rocks: Clays, silts, sands and gravels
(Alluvium). Peats. Raised beaches.

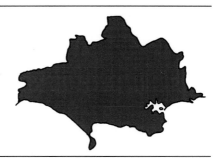

Temperatures which started to fall during the early Tertiary continued their downward trend for the next 60 Ma as the major polar
ice caps grew. Studies suggest an average drop of 10° c in north-west
Europe. The closing chapter of the Cenozoic is the 1.5 Ma called the
Quaternary, which is divided into two periods, the **Pleistocene** and
Holocene. During this time temperature fluctuations became more
extreme and Britain was subjected to successive glaciations.

Despite the relatively short time-span involved, compared to the
missing 38.5 Ma of the previous chapter, significant modifications to
the landscape were achieved. These resulted from the extremes of
climate to which Dorset was subjected, along with rapid changes in
sea level caused by waxing and waning ice sheets, and movements of
the land in response to the increase and decrease of ice-caps in the
north of Britain. Changes in sea level are demonstrated by the two
raised beaches at Portland Bill dating from 210,000 and 125,000 years
ago.

Three major periods of glaciation are recorded in Britain, with
as many as 17 warm/cold fluctuations. Dorset was not covered
by the ice sheets which moved south over much of Britain but
did experience very low temperatures. Ice-caps would have been

maintained at the highest levels with permafrost on other high ground. Because of Dorset's lower latitude, summer warming would have released substantial volumes of water from the ice caps. This created powerful rivers which carried huge quantities of sand and gravel to be deposited as terraces at different heights above sea level particularly along the Frome and other valleys. These represent different stages in the evolution of rivers which were cutting down and back to reach sea level, which was itself rising and falling with each interglacial and glacial phase. The rapid deepening of the valleys and vales caused instability which led to massive landslides, as seen around Shaftesbury and Abbotsbury (see also Chapter 14). Such processes led to large volumes of rock and sediment being transported to lower ground. Today erosion by the sea is the major

Raised Beach (210,000 years before present) at Portland Bill, seen here resting on Portland Stone below the white building.

Looking down on a section of landslip between Charmouth and Lyme Regis.
Extensive mud flows in the area can make for extremely dangerous conditions.

destabiliser of slopes in Dorset; the landslips of the west Dorset coast
are famed for their scale.

The remains of the animals which inhabited this often harsh
landscape are discovered from time to time, including the distinctive grinding teeth and tusks of mammoth and elephant. The
most famous occurrence was the Dewlish Elephant Trench between
Dorchester and Blandford. During the excavation of building-sand, a
narrow fissure was discovered which contained the remains of a
southern elephant dating from a warm phase around 500,000 years
ago. This pre-dated the first major glacial advance.

Exactly when the first people arrived in Dorset is not known.
The first evidence comes from the scatter of flint and chert hand-
axes which are found associated with certain river terrace gravels,
specially around the Devon - Dorset boundary at Broom.

The evolving human population which from time to time inhabited
Dorset would have undoubtedly fluctuated with the climate. During
cold phases, sea level fell, by as much as 120 m. below current
sea level during the last glaciation, and connections with the continent permitted migrations to the less severely affected continent.
The nomadic peoples may have witnessed catastrophic events on an

enormous scale. Research suggests that on at least one occasion a gigantic surge of meltwater and debris flowed down over the Channel plain after the breaching of the 'dam' where the Dover Straits are today. This allowed an enormous volume of meltwater trapped between the North Sea glaciers and the 'dam' to cascade onto the lower Channel basin, gouging great valleys and altering the established drainage pattern.

The last glaciation ended 10,000 years ago. The sea level rose at an average rate of 1 m./100 years. This would have encroached onto the low-lying land at 20 m./year. As this happened, the sea swept the great accumulations of shingle on the Channel plain landwards. For Dorset this was of immense significance, for by 7,000 - 5,000 years ago the Chesil Beach had formed. This great shingle storm beach, of unique scientific importance and international renown, now stretches from Portland, which it connects to the mainland, to West Bay. Along its length the beach protects settlements and the fragile environment of the Fleet, a 13 km. long stretch of fresh to brackish water which runs from Abbotsbury to Smallmouth at Wyke Regis.

There is growing concern that the beach is slowly dwindling. While

J. C. Mansel Pleydell and his team of excavators with the tusk of a southern elephant from the Dewlish Elephant Trench excavation of 1888/9.

The Chesil Beach stretches into the distance in this view from West Weares on the Isle of Portland.

shingle extraction is no longer permitted, alterations to the coast by man has stopped replenishment from cliffs eroding in the west of Dorset and Devon. Rising sea levels coupled with the risk of more frequent and severe storms pose a major threat to the stability of this geomorphological giant.

Like the Chesil Beach we stand on the edge of the unknown. Increasingly our activities are suspected of having far-reaching consequences which are being imposed on the geological continuum, but with what effect we will have to wait and see. We do know that our foundations are both deep and old and that they have shaped Dorset over millions of years without the help of man. They have not finished shaping Dorset yet!

GLOSSARY

ALGAE. Primitive plants which include sea-weeds and plant plankton. See *Coccoliths* and *Stromatolites*.

AMMONITES. Extinct marine invertebrates with a chambered shell which is normally planispirally coiled.

ANTICLINAL see *Anticline*.

ANTICLINE. Strata which have been folded into an arch shape. They range in size from a few metres to tens of kilometres.

ASHLAR STONE. Large blocks of dressed stone used for building.

BASEMENT. The folded and eroded rocks upon which the Permo-Triassic *sediments* rest.

BELEMNITES. Bullet shaped internal shells made of *calcite* belonging to an extinct group of animals related to the modern cuttlefish.

BIVALVES. An abundant group of invertebrate animals which are normally protected by two shells. Present-day examples include cockles, oysters and mussels.

BRACHIOPODS. Marine invertebrates protected by two valves. The resemblance of brachiopods to roman lamps led to them being called lamp shells .

BRECCIA. A sedimentary rock composed of angular fragments from pre-existing rocks cemented by grained sediment.

BRYOZOANS. Small colonial animals which form skeletons of calcium carbonate (*Calcite*) which may encrust solid surfaces or grow in branching tree-like forms.

CALCITE. The crystalline form of calcium carbonate which is an important rock-forming mineral. Limestones are predominantly made of calcite and it forms the hard parts of many invertebrates like *belemnites*, *brachiopods* and *bryozoans*.

CALCIUM CARBONATE see *Calcite*.

CARBONIFEROUS (360-290 MA). A period of geological time during a part of which Britain's deposits of coal were laid down. Carboniferous rocks to the west of Dorset are predominantly marine muds.

CEMENTED. Mineral particles and fragments which are glued together or *lithified* to form a rock by minerals such as *calcite* or *quartz*, deposited from solutions flowing through them.

CHERT. A fine grained rock composed of the mineral silica (see *Quartz*).

Cherts are hard and dense and range in colour from black to brown or yellow. Flint is a purer variety of chert found in the Chalk.

COCCOLITHS. Microscopic rings of *calcite* plates, several of which form the spherical skeleton of a planktonic *algae*.

CONCRETIONS. Usually spherical masses of *cemented* sediment which formed during or after the deposition of the host *sediment* (see also *Septarian nodule*).

CONDENSED. When only very small volumes of *sediment* accumulate over a long period of time, the resulting *sediments* are part of a condensed sequence. Equivalent sediments elsewhere may be hundreds of metres thick.

CONGLOMERATE. A sedimentary rock composed of pebbles from pre-existing rocks *cemented* by fine grained *sediment*.

CONGLOMERATIC. see *Conglomerate*.

CRETACEOUS (136-65 MA). A period of geological time during which environments across Dorset ranged from fully marine to terrestrial. These strata in Dorset, including clays, sands and limestones, are generally well exposed and often very fossiliferous.

CRINOIDS. Also known as sea-lilies, are marine animals related to *echinoids*. They have stalks which support a many armed food-gathering cup.

DEBRIS FLOWS. A poorly sorted mixture of rock fragments and clay, silt and sand, which move under gravity down mountain and hillsides, aided for example by freeze-thaw action and or torrential rain.

DEVONIAN (408-360 MA). A period of geological time during which marine muds, limestones and volcanic rocks were deposited across south-west England.

DOLOMITIC. Describes limestones which are composed of magnesium carbonate rather than *calcium carbonate (calcite)*.

DRILLING MUDS. A specially prepared mixture of ground up rock and mineral material with additions which range from shredded cellophane to the shells of nuts. Used by drilling engineers to lubricate and cool drill bits deep under ground. They also reduce the risk of a blow-outs when gas or oil tries to escape up the hole to the surface.

ECHINOIDS. Echinoids are also known as sea-urchins, a member of the group of animals called echinoderms.

ENCRUSTERS. Animals which grow over solid surfaces, e.g. *bryozoans, serpulid worms*.

FAULT. A fracture in the rocks which allows vertical or horizontal movement to take place. Movement along a fault may be measured in kilometres.

FAULT CONTROLLED DEPOSITION. Faults which move beneath an area where *sediments* are being deposited will cause sediments to thicken on the downthrow side and thin on the rising surface.

FLINT see *Chert*.

GASTROPODS. More commonly known as snails, these are an abundant group of invertebrate animals which are normally protected by spiralled shells.

GEOPHYSICAL SURVEYS. Sophisticated techniques are used to provide information on the rocks below the surface, often at considerable depths, e.g. man-made shockwaves are used to recognise *anticlines* where oil may occur.

GLAUCONITE. A mineral of complex composition occurring as sand-sized grains which vary from light-green to almost black. Their presence in rocks is usually an indication of deposition in the sea.

GONDWANALAND. An ancient super-continent in the southern hemisphere. Antarctica, S. America, Africa, Australia and India were all a part of this great land mass.

HERCYNIAN OROGENY. The mountain building episode in Britain and North West Europe caused by the collision of Gondwanaland and Laurasia.

HOLOCENE (10,000 YEARS AGO TO PRESENT). The period of time during which man has become resident in Dorset. The landscape continues to be modified by the erosion and deposition of sediments.

IGNEOUS INTRUSIONS. Masses of molten rock which move towards, but cool before reaching, the surface. Dartmoor is an example of an igneous intrusion which is now exposed. Granite is an example of an igneous rock.

IRON PYRITES. The mineral iron sulphide, also known as 'fools gold'. This mineral is often abundant in sedimentary rocks, especially clays.

JURASSIC (204-136 MA). A period of geological time during which predominantly marine sands, silts, clays, shales and limestones were deposited across Dorset. The strata are well exposed and often very fossiliferous. The climate was tropical to sub-tropical.

K-T BOUNDARY. The Cretaceous - Tertiary boundary, 65 Ma.

LAURASIA. An ancient super-continent in the northern hemisphere. N. America, Europe and Asia north of the Himalayas were all a part of this great land mass.

LITHIFIED. Literally, turned to stone (*cemented.*)

MATURING. Organic rich *sediments* as they are buried deeper and deeper and the organic material eventually migrates as oil and gas when they are said to be mature.

METAMORPHOSED. Rocks which have been altered by pressure and or heat. Existing minerals may be reformed and new minerals made.

MOLLUSCS. A group of invertebrate animals which include *gastropods, bivalves* and *ammonites.*

MONOCLINE. *Anticlinaly* folded strata where the rocks on each side of the steep middle limb are more or less gently dipping.

NEOGENE (24-1.5 MA). A period of geological time which includes the Miocene and Pliocene periods. No sediments are recognised from this period in Dorset.

OOLITE. A rock composed of *ooliths*.

OOLITHS. Small spheres of *calcium carbonate* which look like the coarse fish roes one can purchase from the fishmonger. The word oolith comes from the Greek 'ooid' which means egg and 'lithos' meaning stone. Thin shells of calcium carbonate are deposited around a sand grain or particle of shell.

OUTLIER. A discrete area of younger rocks which are surrounded by older strata.

PALAEOGENE (65-24 MA). A period of geological time which includes the Palaeocene, Eocene and Oligocene periods. The sediments deposited across Dorset include clays, sands, gravels and limestone representing marine and terrestrial environments. The climate cooled from tropical to temperate at the close.

PANGAEA. The super-continent formed when Gondwanaland and Laurasia were united.

PERMIAN (290-250 MA). A period of geological time during which southern Britain was subjected to desert- like conditions after a period of mountain building.

PERMO-TRIASSIC. That period of geological time covering the Permian and Triassic periods.

PLEISTOCENE (1.5 MA - 10,000 YEARS AGO). The period of geological time during which Britain was subjected to alternating glaciations and warm temperate interludes.

QUARTZ. A variety of silica and an abundant mineral. The major constituent of most sands. Related are *flint* and *chert*.

QUARTZITES. Rocks consisting of grains of *quartz*-sand which have been welded together with more quartz deposited from solution or by grains fusing together along shared surfaces when the grain boundaries may vanish.

SEDIMENTARY STRUCTURE. Evidence of processes which were affecting *sediments* as they were deposited and before they were *lithified*.

SEDIMENTS. Particles of rock or mineral grains ranging from the very small (muds) through silts and sands to larger pebbles, cobbles etc.

SEISMIC SURVEY. Using shock waves to obtain a picture of what lies under our feet.

SEPTARIAN NODULES. Localised enrichment of clays with *calcium carbonate* leads to the formation of spheres or flattened spheres. Loss of water causes a network of concentric and radial fractures to form which may fill with *calcite* giving rise to a septate appearance.

SERPULID WORMS. Marine worms living in often complex *calcium carbonate* tubes which they secrete.

SILICIFIED. Rocks, and especially limestones, which have been replaced by silica (see *Quartz*).

SOLUTION HOLES. These are holes ranging from less than a metre to many tens of metres across and deep, caused by the dissolving of the limestone rock by very weak organic acids in water.

STROMATOLITES. Primitive plants (cyanobacteria) which by non-photosynthetic processes form banded *calcium carbonate*. They are important *sediment* producers.

SYNCLINE. Strata which have been folded into a trough shape. They range in size from a few metres to tens of kilometres.

TECTONIC. Relating to movement of the rocks.

TRACE FOSSILS. Evidence left in *sediments* by many activities of animals such as movement, feeding, protection.

TRANSGRESSION. When sea level rises and more land is covered by the sea; fringing seas become deeper.

TRIASSIC (250-204 MA). A period of geological time during which terrestrial gravels, sands, silts and clays were deposited across Dorset. Salt deposits were laid down. Generally arid but with warm and wet intervals.

TURTLE STONES. see *Septarian nodules*.

UNCONFORMITY. The contact between rocks where sedimentation has not been continuous. A considerable gap in time may be represented. The unconformity may be obvious with folded and eroded rocks overlain by horizontal *sediments* giving an angular unconformity, or bedding may be similar above and below giving a non-angular unconformity when only zone fossils (Chapter 3) allow detection.

FURTHER READING

A colossal literature relating to the geology of Dorset exists and it is not possible to list anything but a few key works.

The *Bibliography and index of Dorset geology* by Jo Thomas, and Paul Ensom, 1989, provides almost 100% coverage of all published and some unpublished aspects up to 1988. Obtainable from the Dorset County Museum, Dorchester. The Museum also has comprehensive displays drawing on its fine collection of geological specimens from the county.

House, M. R., 1993, The Geology of the Dorset Coast. *Geologists Association Guide.* (2nd Edition). ISBN 0 900717 58 0.

Taylor, P. D., (Editor), 1995, *Field Geology of the British Jurassic.* The Geological Society. ISBN 1-897799-41-1.

Publications of the British Geological Survey are another rich source of information:

Melville, R. V. and Freshney, E. C., 1983, *British Regional Geology. Hampshire Basin and adjoining areas.* 6th Edition. HMSO. This general account covers an area including the Isle of Wight and much of Hampshire. ISBN 0 11 884203 X.

Arkell, W. J., 1947, The Geology of the Country around Weymouth, Swanage, Corfe and Lulworth. *Memoir of the Geological Survey.* HMSO.

Bristow, C. R., Barton, C. M., Freshney, E. C., Wood, C. J., Evans, D. J., Cox, B. M., Ivimey-Cook, H. C. and Taylor, R. T., 1995, Geology of the Country around Shaftesbury. *Memoir of the Geological Survey.* HMSO. ISBN 011 884505 5.

Bristow, C. R., Freshney, E. C. and Penn, I. E., 1991, Geology of the Country around Bournemouth. *Memoir of the Geological Survey.* HMSO. ISBN 0 11 884377 X.

Wilson, V., Welch, F. B. A., Robbie, J. A. and Green, G. W., 1958, Geology of the Country around Bridport and Yeovil. *Memoir of the Geological Survey.* HMSO.

The most recent of these provide excellent accounts of the latest advances in our understanding of the geology of parts of Dorset with additional references to work published since the *Bibliography and index of Dorset geology* by Thomas and Ensom.

Geological Survey maps at the scale of 1:50,000 are available for much of the area.

The Natural History Museum's handbooks *British Mesozoic Fossils* and *British Caenozoic Fossils* illustrate many of the fossils which may be found in the rocks of Dorset.

These publications are normally available through book shops and ISBN numbers where available have been given. *The Proceedings of the Dorset Natural History & Archaeological Society*, published annually, regularly carries articles and notes on Dorset geology. Offprints of these are generally available at the Dorset County Museum, in Dorchester. Catalogues of BGS's maps, books and other publications are available on request from: Sales Desk, British Geological Survey, Kingsley Dunham Centre, Keyworth, Nottingham. NG12 5GG. Tel. 0115 936 3241, Fax: 0115 936 3488.

ACKNOWLEDGMENTS

David Burnett generously invited me to write this brief account of the geology of Dorset and my wife Meriel encouraged me to accept the challenge knowing full well what would be involved. Along with our sons, Thomas and James, she has coped admirably with my tunnel vision. I pay tribute to the generations of geologists, professional and amateur, who have observed the geology of Dorset and who continue to unravel its rich and varied history. In writing this account I have drawn on their cumulative knowledge. Thanks to Jo Draper, my father Donald Ensom, Professor Michael House and Richard Tayler who read and constructively commented on the text and to Dr Jerry Hooker for clarification of the Creechbarrow mammals. The author alone accepts responsibility for the information presented. Last but not least, my thanks to the Dorset Natural History & Archaeological Society, who by employing me in 1978, let me open my eyes to the geological wonders of Dorset.

I would like to thank the following for allowing the inclusion of illustrations in their possession or for which they hold the copyright: AMOCO kindly permitted photography of their site at West Chaldon (page 16); BG Exploration and Production Ltd: page 14; Dennis Burden: geological column on page 6, the processes and environments diagram on page 11, the drawing of an ammonite on page 19; Christopher Chaplin: the miniature maps and the general geological map on page 8, (the latter with thanks also to Dr M. E. Cosgrove (Dorset Wildlife Trust); Dorset County Museum: pages 22, 27 (both, G 1240, G 7258), 37, 70 (G 9761), 73 (G 2283), 80: NASA (Don Davis): page 67; The Natural History Museum, London: pages 15, 24, 58 (bottom); The Palaeontological Association kindly sanctioned the use of the illustrations on pages 23 and 56; Richard Tayler: page 41 (also back cover); Colin Varndell: frontispiece, pages 61, 76, 79, 81; Yorkshire Museum: pages 23 (1993.338), 28 (1997.7).

The distribution of the Pre-Permian rocks on the map in Chapter 2 is based on figure 6 from the Memoir of the Geological Survey, Shaftesbury, by C.R. Bristow *et al.* (1995) by permission of the Director, British Geological Survey.